Contents

Seek and Find

Can you find these objects in your book?

page 5

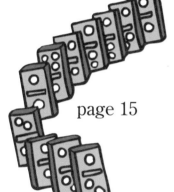
page 15

page 19

page 16

page 11

page 23

Cover illustration by Julia Woolf

Solving Hidden Pictures puzzles develops figure-ground perception and improves the ability to establish object constancy and size relationships. Educators have shown that working on these puzzles can enhance a child's attention to detail, reinforce good work habits, increase word knowledge, and aid in developing self-confidence.

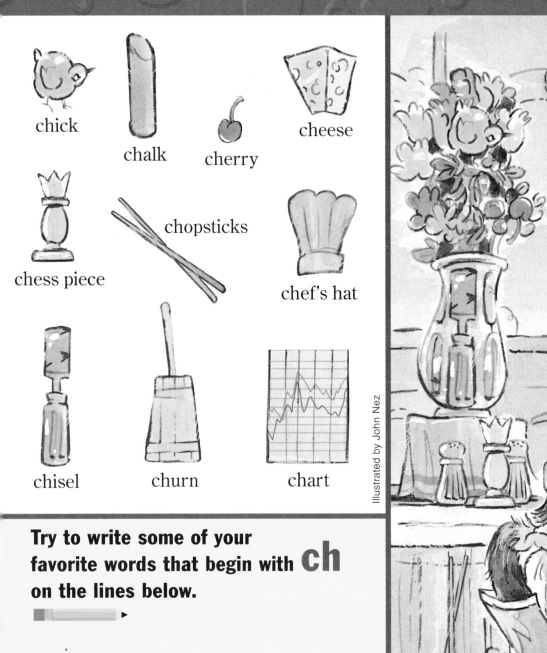

chick

chalk

cherry

cheese

chess piece

chopsticks

chef's hat

chisel

churn

chart

Illustrated by John Nez

Try to write some of your favorite words that begin with ch on the lines below.

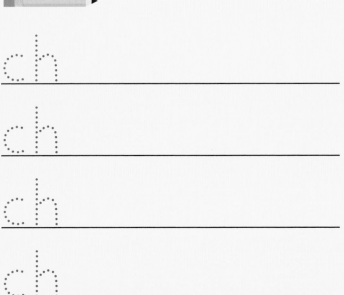

ch _____

ch _____

ch _____

ch _____

Can you find the 10 objects hidden in the picture that begin with the letters ch? Charge! Answers on page 30

3

These 8 funny things are happening in the scene.
Can you find them all? Answers on page 30

Imagine and Draw

What is the silliest thing you might see riding a bicycle? Draw a picture of it here.

| CRAYON |

Illustrated by Viki Woodworth

6 Fun at Recess

After a rainy week, everyone is glad to be outside for recess.

Can you find these hidden objects on the next page? Answers on page 30

celery stalk

computer mouse

eyeglasses

baseball bat

mushroom

crown

feather

baseball glove

Scavenger Hunt

Here are some more things to find:

Two lunch boxes

A broom

A book

Two birds

A heart

Two balls

Three baseball caps

A whistle

Can you find the hidden objects below? When you finish, you can color in the

ART FAIR

rest of the scene. | CRAYON | Answers on page 30   Illustrated by Larry Daste

Color in a ladybug in this box each time you find a ladybug in the picture.   CRAYON

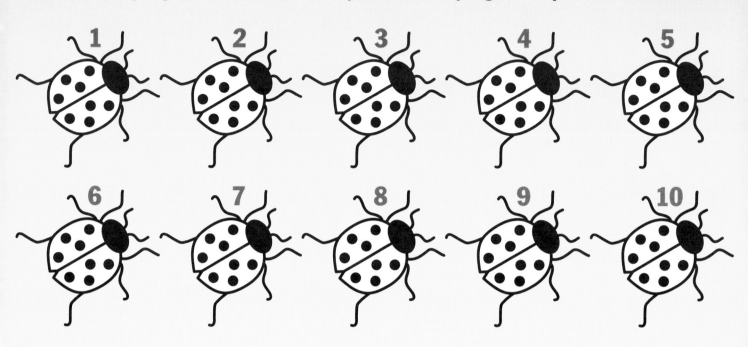

Connect the dots from Ⓐ to Ⓩ. When you finish, you will see another insect that flies. ▶

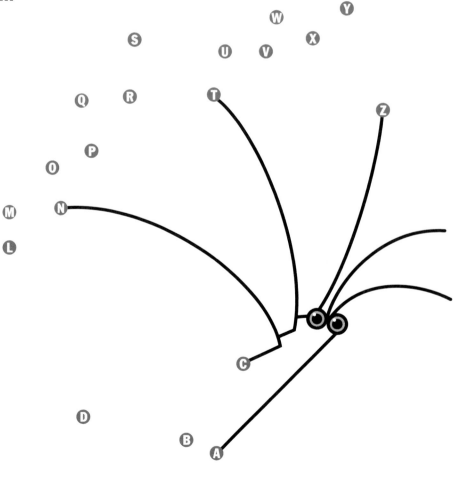

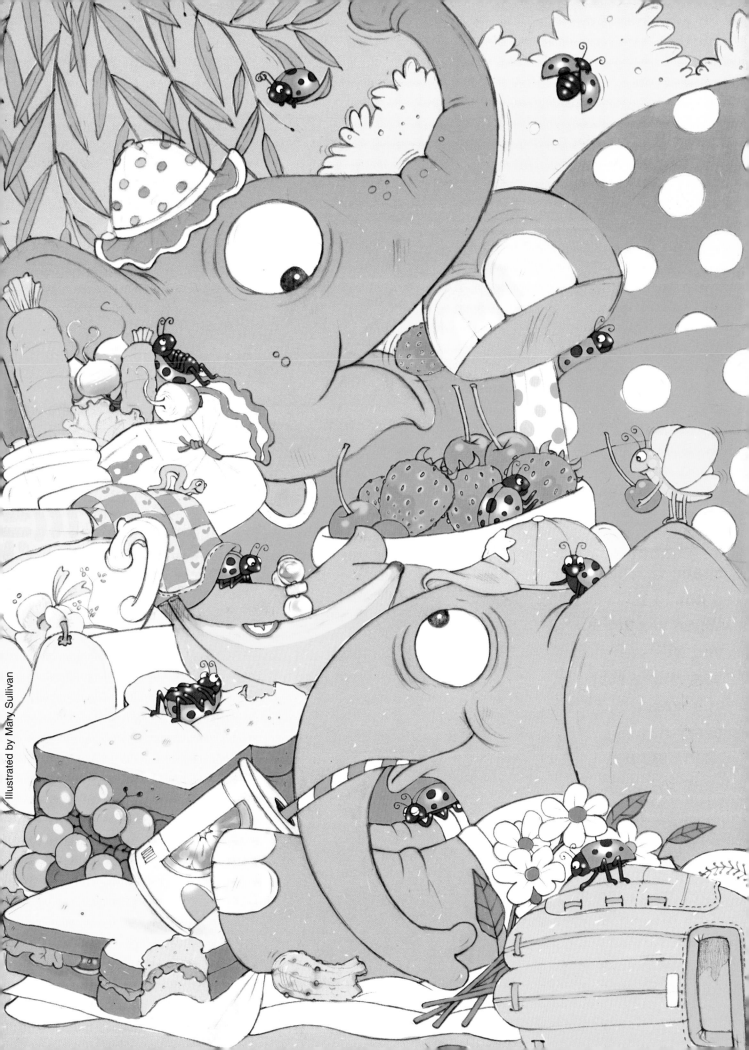

Hank and Lily are helping their dad wash the family car.

Can you find 8 hidden objects on the next page? Answers on page 31

ice-cream cone

slice of cake

fishhook

key

tweezers

flashlight

sailboat

artist's brush

Color in each shape that has a dot in it. When you finish, you will see something that you wash every day.

| CRAYON |

**Hidden Pictures time to rhyme.
You can find them every time.**

Do you see a **roller skate**

And a fancy dinner  **plate**?

Where did the lazy **lizard** go

And some ribbon in a **bow**?

Now look about for a 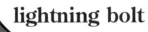 **lightning bolt**

And the 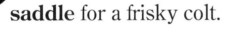 **saddle** for a frisky colt.

Find an **envelope** for a letter

And a 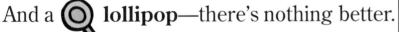 **lollipop**—there's nothing better.

Don't stop until you find a **mug**

And a **teddy bear** to hug.

**You first found one and then the rest.
Hip! Hip! Hooray! You are the best!**

Answers on page 31

Illustrated by Judith Moffatt and Bill Hoffman

DOMINOES

Can you find the hidden objects below? When you finish, you can color in the

Gary and his mother are buying a special dessert.
What do you think they will choose?

Can you find these items in the picture on the next page?
Be sure to find the right number of each. Answers on page 31

1 pink cake

2 heart cookies

3 pies

4 star cookies

5 muffins

6 loaves of bread

Draw a piece of your favorite cake or pie. CRAYON

Illustrated by Monica Wellington

The Best Thing

Monica watched the parade with her grandmother. "I like to hear the 🥁 **drum**," Monica told Grandma as a marching band went by. "I like the way it goes *rum, tum, tum.*" Monica smiled.

"There's something I like better," said Grandma.

Next came the clowns. "I like clowns," Monica said. "The one with the red 🎀 **bow tie** squirted his friend with a ❀ **flower**." Monica laughed.

"There's something I like better," said Grandma.

Next, the floats rode by. "My favorite one looks like a 🚤 **boat**," said Monica. "It has a big 🐙 **octopus** throwing 🍬 **candy**." Monica smiled as she caught a piece.

The fire trucks drove by last.

"I like the shiny fire trucks," Monica said. "Look, there's a 🐕 **dog** wearing a little 👒 **fire fighter's hat**!" Monica smiled and waved at the fire fighters.

"There's something I like better," said Grandma.

"But the parade's over," said Monica. "What do you like best?"

Grandma laughed. "I like your big, happy smile," she said. "That's the best thing of all."

A Hidden Pictures® Rebus Story by Clare Mishica

Illustrated by Ellen Appleby

question mark pail goblet spoon baseball doughnut

Each object is hidden two times—once in each scene. We found and circled the doughnuts. Can you find the others? Answers on page 32

cell phone   drumstick   paintbrush   lollipop   screwdriver   bell

Can you find the hidden objects below? When you finish, you can color in the

Camille takes pictures wherever she goes.
Today she is at a soccer match.

Can you find these shapes in the picture on the next page? Answers on page 32

What is your favorite sport? Draw a picture of it here.

|| CRAYON ||

Be sure to write your name on your drawing when you are finished.

Hidden Pictures®

These dancers are practicing for a special holiday show.

There are 12 objects hidden in this picture. How many can you find?

Answers on page 32

dog bone

banana

comb

flower

snail

The names of the 12 objects are hidden below. Some are across. Others are up and down. Find and circle each word.

t	b	z	s	n	a	i	l
o	a	x	e	g	g	y	p
o	n	j	b	a	l	l	a
t	a	d	j	k	q	x	p
h	n	o	f	x	k	p	e
b	a	g	l	o	v	e	r
r	q	b	o	c	r	n	c
u	y	o	w	o	i	c	l
s	x	n	e	m	n	i	i
h	j	e	r	b	g	l	p

paper clip

ring

egg

pencil

glove

toothbrush

ball

Answers

Cover

Hidden Pictures® ABC pages 2–3

Silly Cycling page 5

Fun at Recess pages 6–7

Scavenger Hunt

Two lunch boxes
A girl is touching one.
One is near the backpack.

A broom
It is leaning against a tree.

A book
Look on the ground.

Two birds
One is in a tree. One is flying.

A heart
It is on a girl's shirt.

Two balls
A girl is holding one.
One is on the ground.

Three baseball caps
Two boys and a girl are each
wearing one.

A whistle
Look at the teacher.

At the Art Fair pages 8–9

Ladybug Search pages 10–11

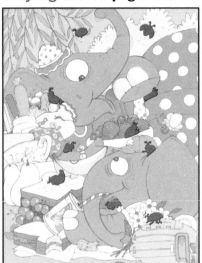

It's a butterfly!

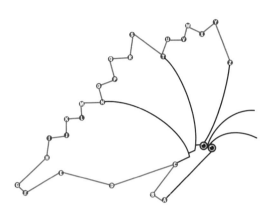

Car Wash pages 12–13

Hidden Pictures® Rhymes pages 14–15

It's a hand!

Flea Market pages 16–17

Betty's Bakery page 19

Answers

The Best Thing page 21

Double Hidden Pictures® pages 22–23

New Neighbors pages 24–25

Find the Shapes page 27

Hidden Pictures® Hidden Words pages 28–29